This book belongs to

_____

Please be kind to this book!

We thank the monks of Great St. Bernard for the pictures
and text which they made available to us,
and for their friendly advice during the production of this book.

ISBN 978-3-8157-2040-0
© 2000 Coppenrath Verlag GmbH & Co. KG, Münster
Baumgartner Bücher, Dietikon
Translated from the German by Barbara A. Emmel
German original edition © 1999 Coppenrath Verlag GmbH & Co. KG, Münster
Baumgartner Bücher, Dietikon
All rights reserved
Printed in Belgium
www.coppenrath.de

BARRY

Rescuer on Four Paws

A true story
retold by Barbara Cratzius
with illustrations by Ursula Blancke

BAUMGARTNER / COPPENRATH

It was on a cold, dark night that three small St. Bernard puppies came into the world, in a solitary monastery high up in the Alps.

One of them was Barry.

The puppies' mother lay in freshly laid straw and lovingly licked her newborn young. Next to her knelt the young monk Benno. He stroked her fur gently. "What beautiful, healthy puppies," he said softly.

"This one here was the last to be born. But he is the biggest and the strongest. He looks almost like a little bear, with his large head and his broad muzzle."

Benno cradled the little puppy in his arm. "I will call you Barry, little bear. That name suits you well." The little puppy raised his head, as if he already recognized his name,

and snuggled up to

his new friend.

Outside, the spring wind rattled the window shutters. In the valley below, it was already warm. But here in St. Bernard Pass, the snow and ice would last a long time yet.

Finally summer came, and the little dogs could romp in the mountain pastures. Barry charged ahead of the others. Ever curious, he bounded through the fragrant grass towards the mountain stream. How the water foamed and sprayed! Brrr – it was cold! Barry shook his fur. Then Benno took a stick and threw it far across the mountain meadow. The puppies immediately chased after it. Barry was the fastest. He laid the stick proudly before his master. "Good Barry," said Benno. Benno showed the young St. Bernards each and every path in the mountains. By the time the short summer came to an end, the young dogs could find their way reliably back to the hospice, the house of the monks.

One morning the whole world suddenly turned white. The first snow –
what an adventure for the young dogs! They snapped at the thick
snowflakes as they were falling. With their paws, they thrust up cold,
white clumps of snow and sniffed at them. They rolled excitedly in the
loosely packed snow. At first, they sank up to their stomachs and had
trouble climbing out again. But Barry watched carefully how his mother
and his father managed in the snow. He learned quickly to place his
paws in such a way that he no longer sank deep into the snow.

"Good dog," praised Benno. And after just a little while, Barry could plow through the snow with his broad chest just as well as his parents could, and push the snow aside with his strong paws. In this way, he left behind a path in which a person could walk. "Good dog," cried Benno and petted him.

Benno was a patient, but also a strict teacher. When the young St. Bernards were grown, they would help to save people's lives in the mountains. Therefore they had to learn one thing above all else: to obey the monks' every word. That wasn't always easy for the high-spirited Barry. But he knew that Benno was his best friend.

Dark came early during the winter days. One evening, Benno sat with the other monks in front of the fire and listened to the roar of an icy storm. "I must go out onto the mountain," he said suddenly. "Perhaps in the darkness travelers have gotten lost in the snow. Today I will take Barry with me. He has grown big enough now."

The trail over the pass was completely snowed in. But, with his keen nose, Barry found the path and ran swiftly forward. Then all at once he stopped. Benno almost fell over him. "What's wrong, Barry?" asked Benno. The dog had his tail tucked tightly in, he was trembling all over, and he began to bark excitedly.

A moment later, a thundering sound and snow spray filled the air. An enormous white wall of snow veiled the mountain peak. Barry had sensed it: not far from them, an avalanche had come crashing down. But fortunately that night, no travelers were on their way over the pass.

The next day, Benno said, "Today we should find out whether the young dogs can now scent a person in the snow." Together with several other monks, he trudged off. Far from the hospice, the men dug a deep burrow, into which Benno climbed. "Don't send the dogs out too soon," he called. "My tracks on the path should have long disappeared. And it will be some time before my scent wafts up from this hole."

"But we are not going to let you freeze here," protested the others and closed up the burrow.

A little while later, they sent the dogs out on the search. All the tracks on the paths were covered up by freshly fallen snow. But Barry, nose fast to the ground, ran unerringly forward. Even from afar, he could scent the place where his friend was buried. There he started to bark and excitedly began to dig in the snow. Finally Benno could free himself from his burrow. Barry almost did a somersault for joy. Over and over, he jumped up on his friend and licked his frozen fingers.

"Good dog," Benno praised him, "good Barry! You're going to rescue many, many more people from the snow."

Barry became Benno's trusty companion on his daily journeys through
the mountains. Yet there was always more for Barry to learn. One freez-
ing cold, moonlit night, they met a young workman who was crossing
the pass. He was carrying a heavy pack on his back. "Greetings!" Benno
called to him. "Come with us to the hospice, you can rest there over-
night." The wayfarer thankfully handed his pack over to the young
monk, for they still had a long way ahead of them. Suddenly, the man
collapsed from exhaustion and could not go any farther. In urgent haste,
Benno tied the worker's neckerchief tightly onto Barry's collar. "Run
quickly, Barry," he cried, "bring help!" But Barry didn't understand what
Benno wanted him to do. He had learned never to abandon his master.
Over and over, he took just a few steps forward and then turned back
to Benno. But finally he grasped the idea and then ran with leaps and
bounds to the hospice.

Because of the strange neckerchief, the monks realized immediately that something must have happened. Barry led them to Benno and the young man was saved. "That was your first great deed, Barry," said Benno softly and stroked his intelligent dog.

"Come, Barry," Benno called a couple of days later. "We have to go out. A group of bearers needs to be led over the pass." It had begun to snow, and a thick fog veiled the mountains. But Barry loved this kind of weather. Wagging his tail, he sprang through the deep snow, so quickly that Benno could hardly follow him. Soon they saw the heavily laden men emerge in the distance. "You have strayed from the path," shouted Benno from afar. "Follow me and my dog!" Then suddenly Barry pricked up his ears, barked loudly, and ran forward even more quickly than before. "Slow down, slow down!" called one of the bearers. "We cannot walk so fast." But Benno shouted, "Run as fast as you can. Follow Barry's trail exactly!"

At that very moment, a powerful avalanche came crashing down from the peak and buried some of the men under it. The bearers stared in horror at the white mass of snow that had fallen just behind them. "Paul! Alfred! Carl!" cried the leader of the group. But all around them, icy stillness reigned.

Barry ran back and began to paw at the snow and to dig. But Benno cried, "We can't do it alone, Barry! Run and bring help!" Like lightning, Barry ran back to the hospice. He scratched at the door and barked. The brothers hurried out and loaded up the sleds with shovels and poles. Together with the other dogs, they followed Barry through the driving snow. In the meantime, the bearers had put down their loads. They sat there in a state of shock, while the dogs searched the white expanse.

Barry was the first to bark loudly. The monks ran immediately to the spot and stuck their poles carefully into the deep snow. Benno felt his pole touch something solid. "Here," he shouted, "dig, dig!" Within a few moments, they freed the first buried man. Barry licked the man's frozen face until he opened his eyes. The dogs continued to search and found both other men, still alive. The monks brought the men to the hospice on sleds, where they could warm themselves up and rest.

One evening Barry kept jumping up restlessly and running to the door, whimpering. "Wait, Barry," cried Benno, "I'll get the lantern." But Benno had opened the door just slightly, when Barry flashed by him and disappeared into the darkness. It was stormy that night. The driving snow swept across the slopes. Barry pressed sturdily forward, foot by foot, against the snowstorm, his nose to the ground. He ran straight ahead, then stopped, made a half circle, stopped again and sniffed. Then he sprang forward and barked as if possessed.

A child lay in the deep snow, not moving. Barry licked the child's hands
and his face. Again and again, he nudged the child with his nose until
the boy stirred. The boy was completely stiff from the cold. Barry lay
down by his side to give him warmth.
With difficulty, the child stretched out his hands and took hold of the
dog's soft fur. Unafraid of the large animal, he climbed onto Barry's back
and held fast to his collar. Then Barry stood up carefully and carried the
boy all the way back to the hospice.

Full of concern, Benno had been pacing around the house again and again. Now he ran towards Barry and the little boy. "But that's little Mario from the mountain farm," he cried in wonder. "He comes here in summer sometimes and brings us butter. Someone must send word to his parents right away. Tomorrow we will take Mario home. It's a good thing you found him, Barry!" Benno carried the boy to the warm fire. Barry lay down right next to the boy and guarded his sleep.
"We have never had such an intelligent rescue dog as Barry!" said Benno. He bent down to Barry and petted him and praised him. Barry pricked up his ears and thumped his tail happily.

For twelve years, Barry
accompanied his friend Benno. He saved more than forty lives and his
name was known throughout the land. Barry's young offspring romped
happily around their famous father. Soon they too would learn to follow
a trail in the deep snow.

When Barry became old and weak, and was scarcely able to go outside anymore, the monks lovingly cared for him. One day a man from Berne who loved animals came to the hospice. "Let me take Barry down into the valley," he offered. "I will take good care of him." With heavy hearts, the monks bade Barry farewell. And so Barry spent his last years in the city of Berne, far from his mountain home.

But Barry will never be forgotten. Even today, little St. Bernards come into the world up in the hospice in St. Bernard Pass. And the best of the litter is always given the name Barry, in memory of the courageous rescuer of many people's lives.

If you should happen to see a St. Bernard, ask what its name is. Maybe it is a descendant of the famous Barry!

Epilogue

After his death, Barry was kept for posterity. His body was embalmed in the Natural History Museum of Berne and exhibited for viewing by the admirers of the legendary rescue dog.

A museum about the history of the St. Bernards and their achievements as "guardian angels of the mountains" is part of the hospice in the Great St. Bernard Pass. One can also visit the kennels there, where St. Bernards are still bred today. Each year there are fifteen to twenty puppies. They are eagerly awaited by animal lovers and brought from Switzerland into many other countries. They prefer living where there is a lot of snow and where the summers are not too hot.

Some of them are trained, even today, to become avalanche dogs. Today, German Shepherds also help in the rescue of people buried by snow. They are lighter and more nimble than the St. Bernards and therefore can be transported more easily in helicopters.

But the courageous and intelligent Barry, who, together with many of his kind, did his utmost to help people in danger at a time when technical aids were not available, will never be forgotten.